Mistie Goes Sailing

Written by
Catherine Shaw

Illustrated by
Steve Goodwin

Hello everyone, my name is Colin. I live in a small fishing village called Tideswell.

I work as a Coastguard with my dog Rocky. I have to make sure that people are safe when they are at sea, on the cliffs or on the beach.

If anyone is in trouble I can contact my friends who are always ready to help.

Now read how

Mistie Goes Sailing

It was a warm golden morning.

Colin the Coastguard and his dog Rocky were on their way to Pebble Island.

They were going to watch the Tideswell Yacht Race from the Old Lighthouse.

Tideswell
Yacht Race
Today

Meanwhile, in Tideswell Harbour, the boats were being prepared for the race.

No-one saw a little cat called Mistie leap aboard one of the yachts. She was looking for a comfy place to snooze away the day.

As soon as Colin and Rocky reached Pebble Island, they jumped on to Colin's quad bike and sped away from the jetty.

"We must be quick," said Colin, "we don't want to miss the start of the race."

By the time the race was about to start, Mistie was already fast asleep.

START

TIDESWELL

528

271

174

BOO

The starting cannon was fired...

6

The yachts raced along, skimming the waves. A strong wind was blowing and the sea was rough.

Mistie woke up in a daze, peeped out of the cabin and was spotted by one of the crew!

"We have a stowaway on board!" he called excitedly.

8

Finally, Colin and Rocky reached the Old Lighthouse.

"Quick, up the stairs Rocky," said Colin, "we'll be able to get a better view of the yachts when we've climbed to the top."

As Mistie's yacht sailed past the Old Lighthouse...

CLUNK! CLONK! KERDONK!

With a loud bang and a jolt, the yacht crashed into some floating planks of wood.

The rudder broke. Oh no! Now the yacht could not be steered.

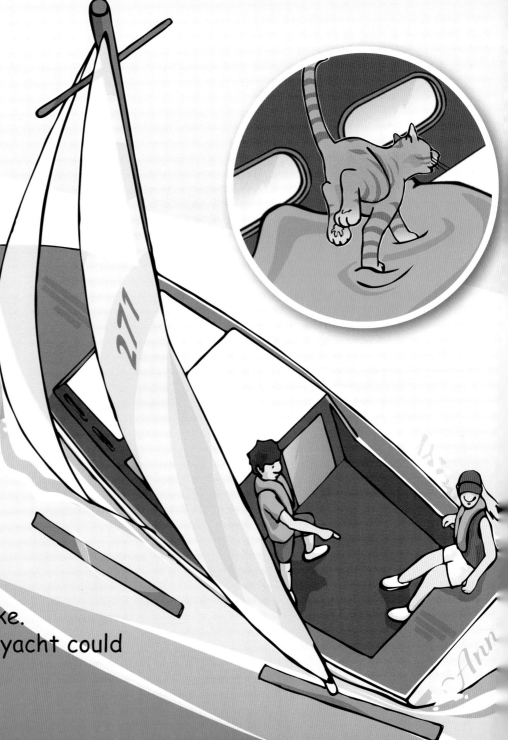

Poor Mistie was so scared! She scampered, slithered and slid all around the cabin.

What should she do?
Where could she go?

Colin could see what had happened to the yacht.

"We must call out the lifeboat," he said, "that yacht's in trouble."

He phoned Goodwin, the Lifeboat Coxswain and asked for his help.

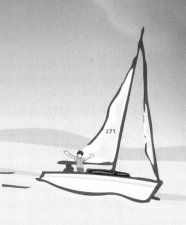

"I'll launch the lifeboat straightaway!" said Goodwin.

12

Moments later, Goodwin's lifeboat raced down the slipway. It plunged into the water with a...

wooosh... swooosh...

The lifeboat quickly arrived beside the damaged yacht.

Goodwin called out to the crew, "Catch this rope! Tie it to your yacht then we'll tow you back to Tideswell Harbour!"

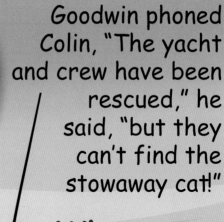

Goodwin phoned Colin, "The yacht and crew have been rescued," he said, "but they can't find the stowaway cat!"

Where was Mistie hiding?

As Goodwin towed the yacht back to Tideswell Harbour, he met Colin and Rocky who were returning from Pebble Island.

The wind had eased and the sea had became calm once again. The dark clouds were drifting away and the sun had begun to shine.

The yacht's crew were safe!

But where was Mistie?

"Where is the little stowaway cat?" asked Colin.

"I can't see her," said Goodwin.

"She's not on deck!" said one crew member.

"She's not in the cabin!" said the other.

Then...

...they looked up.

Poor Mistie!

She was clinging to the top of the mast.

"There she is!" exclaimed Goodwin.

Mistie was too frightened to move!

How could they get her down?

But then...

...Slippy the Seagull flew past with a fish in his beak.

Slippy saw Mistie, 'squawked' and let go of the fish.

As it dropped past Mistie's nose, the smelly fish was too good to ignore!

She stuck out a paw to catch it, lost her grip on the mast and...

...tumbled towards the deck with a scrambling, slithering slide and plopped into Goodwin's arms!

Mistie wasn't hurt. But where was that lovely smelly fish?

"Wow Goodwin, that was a brilliant catch!" cheered Colin.

Rocky barked and wagged his tail.

Everyone was thrilled that Mistie was down from the mast.

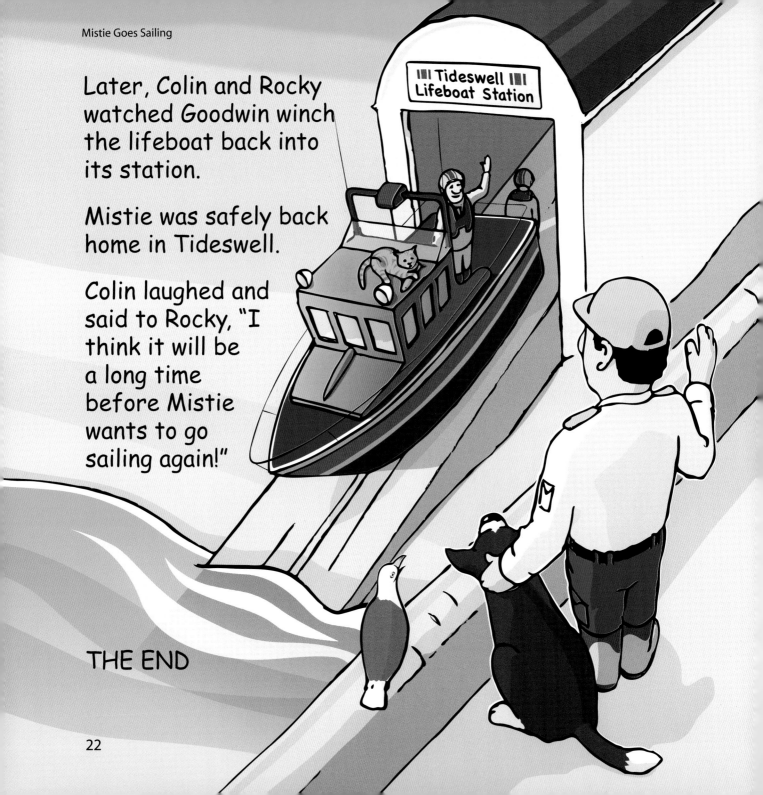

Later, Colin and Rocky watched Goodwin winch the lifeboat back into its station.

Mistie was safely back home in Tideswell.

Colin laughed and said to Rocky, "I think it will be a long time before Mistie wants to go sailing again!"

THE END

Your Search Mission!

A. What is the colour of the bucket on the deck of the yacht on page 4?

B. How many yachts can you see starting the race on page 6?

C. What is the number on the sail on page 8?

D. How many crew members are on the Lifeboat on page 13?

E. What is the name of the Tideswell Lifeboat?

F. What colour are the stripes on the Old Lighthouse?

G. What is the shape of the blue and white sail on page 6?

H. What was Mistie clinging to on page 18?

I. How many times can you see or catch a glimpse of Mistie, throughout the whole book? (Look very carefully on pages 8 and 16)

J. What is Mistie holding on page 22?

Answers: A = Yellow, B = 6, C = 271, D = 3, E = Tilly-Rose, F = Red, G = Triangle, H = The Mast, I = 17, J = A fish